One Woolly Wombat

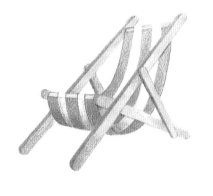

Omnibus Books
175–177 Young Street, Parkside SA 5063
an imprint of Scholastic Australia Pty Ltd (ABN 11 000 614 577)
PO Box 579, Gosford NSW 2250.
www.scholastic.com.au

Part of the Scholastic Group
Sydney • Auckland • New York • Toronto • London • Mexico City •
New Delhi • Hong Kong • Buenos Aires • Puerto Rico

First published in 1982.
First published in paperback in 1983.
First published in this edition in 2014.
Text and illustrations copyright © Kerry Argent, 1982.

National Library of Australia Cataloguing-in-Publication entry
Argent, Kerry.
One Woolly Wombat.
ISBN 978 1 74299 047 7.
1. Animals – Australia – Juvenile literature.
2. Counting – Juvenile literature. I. Title.
513.211

Kerry Argent used colour pencil and watercolour
for the illustrations in this book.
Typeset in Abadi MT Condensed and Curlz MT.
Printed in China by RR Donnelley.

10 9 8 7 6 5 4 3 2 1   14 15 16 17 18 19 20/ 0

One Woolly Wombat

KERRY ARGENT

An Omnibus Book from Scholastic Australia

One woolly wombat
sunning
by the sea

Two cuddly koalas
sipping
gumnut tea

3

Three warbling magpies
waking up
the sun

Four thumping kangaroos
dancing
just for fun

5

Five pesky platypuses
splashing
with their feet

Six cheeky possums
looking for
a treat

Seven emus running …
in and out
the bush

8

Eight spiky echidnas
eating ants —
whoosh

Ten giggly kookaburras
writing
riddle books

Eleven dizzy dingoes
twirling
with their paws

Twelve crazy cockatoos
counting
on their claws

Thirteen hopping mice
picking
desert pea

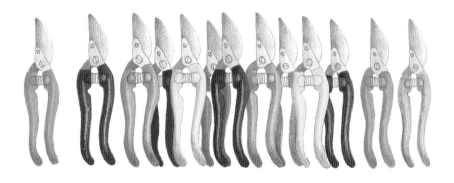

14

Fourteen slick seals
heading out
to sea